Contents

The answers can be found in a pull-out section
in the middle of this book.

How to use this book

Writing non-fiction (pages 8–16)

(1) **Definition** and **Purpose** – This describes the topic simply and explains why it is important.

(2) **Text plan** – This flow chart gives a step-by-step guide to help you plan your writing.

(3) **Guided writing** – A piece of writing based on the text plan with additional assistance.

(4) **Independent writing** – This gives further opportunities for writing long and short pieces of a similar style.

Writing fiction (pages 17–25)

(1) **Revision notes** – Supportive notes that give brief guidance on the writing tasks below.

(2) **Activity choice** – A range of three activities to complete as either a short (20 minutes) or long (45 minutes) piece of writing.

(3) **Guided writing question** – An exercise to be completed in a particular genre.

(4) **Story scaffold** – Provides structure and support, as well as space to plan your writing. Answers provide more detail on writing style and structure.

(5) **Independent writing** – A range of three independent writing activities that can be completed as part of a short or long task.

ACHIEVE LEVEL 5

ENGLISH
Practice
Questions

Carol Matchett
Updated by Madeleine Barnes
Series Editor: Richard Cooper

RISING STARS

Rising Stars UK Ltd, 7 Hatchers Mews, Bermondsey Street, London SE1 3GS

www.risingstars-uk.com

All facts are correct at time of going to press.

First published 2002
Second edition 2008
This edition 2010
Reprinted 2011 (twice), 2012

Text, design and layout © Rising Stars UK Ltd

First edition written by: Sheila Hentall and Helen Ward
Second edition written by: Carol Matchett
Educational consultant: Lorna Pepper
Third edition updated by: Madeleine Barnes
Project management and editorial: Bruce Nicholson
Illustrations: Phill Burrows, Clive Wakfer, Julian Baker
Design: Clive Sutherland
Cover design: Burville-Riley Partnership

Acknowledgements
p46 Photos iStock; p46 Web page frame ssuaphotos;
p46 Reproduced with kind permission of the Hawking Centre,
Leeds Castle, www.thehawkingcentre.co.uk; p48 Extract from
www.jubileebooks.co.uk; p52 First Day At School by Roger
McGough from In the Glassroom (© Roger McGough 1976) is
printed by permission of United Agents (www.unitedagents.co.uk)
on behalf of Roger McGough; p54 Seasick by Nick Toczek first
appeared in his collection of animal poems, Never Stare At A
Grizzly Bear (Macmillan Children's Books 2000) and was more
recently included in Hogs'n'Dogs'n'Slugs'n'Bugs (Caboodle Books
2008), republished as Cats'n'Bats'n'Slugs'n'Bugs (Caboodle Books
2009)

Every effort has been made to trace copyright holders and obtain
their permission for the use of copyright material. The authors and
publishers will gladly receive information enabling them to rectify
any error or omission in subsequent editions.

British Library Cataloguing in Publication Data
A CIP record for this book is available from the British Library.

ISBN 978-1-84680-778-7

Printed by Craft Print International Ltd, Singapore

Reading comprehension (pages 44–55)

(1) **The text** – A range of texts are given, including fiction, non-fiction and poetry.

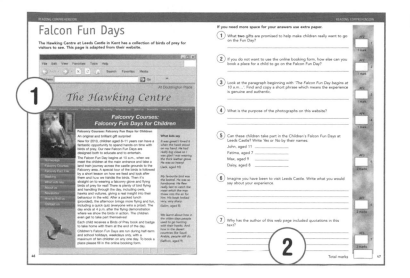

(2) **The questions** – Comprehension questions that allow you to demonstrate your Level 5 reading skills. Number of marks available and space to complete answers are given.

Additional support

Punctuation (pages 31–35)

A range of exercises covering key Level 5 punctuation, including work on the use of ellipses, dashes and semi-colons. It also includes a quick punctuation test.

Vocabulary (pages 36–39)

These vocabulary exercises focus on improving your writing by making sure that 'every word counts'. Each section has a brief explanation, followed by exercises in developing and using Level 5 vocabulary.

Spelling practice (pages 40–41)

These exercises are designed to give useful practice in the more difficult areas of spelling – plurals, tenses and common errors.

Reviewing your work (pages 42–43)

Supportive notes describing how to review your writing continually (especially in tests).

About the National Tests

Key facts

* The Key Stage 2 National Tests take place in the summer term in Year 6. You will be tested on Maths and English.

* The tests take place in your school and will be marked by examiners – not your teacher!

* Individual scores are not made public. However, a school's combined scores are published in what are commonly known as 'league tables'.

The English National Tests

You will take four tests in English. These are designed to test your reading, writing and spelling. Your handwriting will also be assessed through the Longer Writing Task – so remember to keep your writing neat.

The Writing Tasks

There are two Writing Tasks – one shorter task and one longer task.

Make sure you read both tasks carefully. Find out **what** you have to write, **why** you are writing it and **who** you are writing it for. This will help you to decide how to organise your writing and what style you need to use.

The Shorter Writing Task is 20 minutes long. Still spend two or three minutes planning or gathering your thoughts on what you are going to write. Think also about what style you need and how to make your writing effective in a short amount of time.

Once you have decided **what** you are going to write, you can really focus on **how to say it** – making sure you sound like a Level 5 writer!

Remember to leave a few minutes at the end to reread and check your writing, e.g. for missing punctuation.

Make sure your writing has a strong opening and a strong ending.

The Longer Writing Task is 45 minutes long. Spend about 10 minutes planning what you are going to write and how you will order and organise your ideas. Make brief notes on the planning sheet so you can follow them as you write.

The Writing Tasks – continued

Where to go to get help

Pages 8–16 give you advice and opportunities to practise writing non-fiction texts. There are some short tasks and some long tasks.

Pages 17–22 give you an opportunity to practise short narrative tasks, while pages 23–25 provide longer tasks where you need to plan and write complete narratives in 45 minutes.

Pages 26–39 will help you improve your sentence structure, punctuation and vocabulary choices to make your writing more effective.

The Reading Test

This test assesses your reading comprehension. It will last one hour; 15 minutes reading time and 45 minutes to answer the questions. In this test you will be given a series of texts to read and an answer booklet. Remember to use the texts to answer the questions. Find which part of the text a question refers to. Reread that part of the text, thinking about the question and how to answer it.

Remember to look at how many marks each question is worth. This gives you a clue about the length or type of answer you need to give.

Work through the questions in order, but if you really get stuck don't waste time, move on. You can always go back if you think of an answer later.

Where to go to get help

Pages 44–55 give you advice on the types of questions you will be asked and practice in answering them.

The Spelling Test

The Spelling Test is 15 minutes long. Your test paper will have the text of a passage with some words missing. Your teacher will read the complete passage (or play a CD of someone else reading it). You will then hear the passage a second time, during which you have to write the missing words in the spaces on your test paper.

Where to go to get help

Pages 40–41 will remind you of some rules and common errors and give you practice in spelling.

Writing non-fiction

The passive voice in impersonal writing

Non-fiction writing often needs an impersonal tone, e.g. when writing formal reports, explanations or discussions. The passive voice can help to make your writing sound less personal, e.g. *A letter was sent* rather than *I sent a letter*. This tone is important because it gives an air of authority to your writing and makes you sound fair.

Practise writing impersonally by working through these examples.

Rewrite these sentences.

(1) We will hold the workshop in the school hall. The teachers have planned a range of practical activities for the afternoon. The school will provide all the books and materials.

The The workshop will be held in the school hall.

(2) Some people hunt whales so they can use them in scientific research. People also hunt whales for meat. Hunters can take several hundred whales in a season. Lots of people think this is wrong.

Whales are hunted for use in scientific research.

(3) We collect unwanted clothing and we put it into bags. Next some of us sort the clothes and separate them into different boxes. Finally Mrs Wilkins takes the boxes to the charity shop.

Unwanted clothing is collected and put into bags.

(4) If you follow basic hygiene rules you can avoid food poisoning. We display these rules in the kitchen area.

Food poisoning can be avoided by following basic hygiene rules.

Using the right voice – formal and informal

Level 5 writers must be able to choose the right level of formality for their writing. This depends on their audience and purpose. Non-fiction writing often requires a formal tone. Using the passive voice is important and so is choosing the right vocabulary.

- **Do not** use informal 'street talk', everyday words or flowery description.

- **Do** use formal words, technical words relating to the subject and factual description.

Rewrite these sentences using appropriate vocabulary.

1 The sand spider can be really teeny or as big as a 10p piece. It digs a hole in the soft sand and waits inside the hole for a foolish insect to walk by and then gobbles it up. If it bites you, it can kill you.

The sand spider varies in size from just a few metres and to a maximum of 3cm across.
It

2 There has been a lot of talk about closing down our local post office. The fight to stop it has been in all the papers and we really hope the council will change their minds.

The closure of the local post office has caused considerable debate.

3 We hope to put up some lights to stop kids breaking in and pulling up the plants. We will get some adults to help us out with all this work.

We propose installing security lighting to deter vandals.

4 Polar bears have cuddly fur coats to keep them snug in the chilly winds. Their coats are as white as snow so it is difficult to see them in the stunning ice landscape that is the Arctic.

Polar bears have thick fur to keep them well insulted against the icy winds.

Tense

Many non-fiction texts, such as reports and explanations, are written in the present tense. Recounts are written in the past tense. Sometimes you need to shift between tenses for a particular reason.

| Tip | ★ Remember, the future tense is formed with modal verbs, such as *will* and *shall*. |

Write a sentence to show how you might use each tense in these texts.

1 An author's autobiography reflecting on his/her time at school

Past: _____

Present: _____

Future: _____

2 An information leaflet for a living museum

Past: _____

Present: _____

Future: _____

3 An article in a magazine discussing transport in your local area

Past: _____

Present: _____

Future: _____

4 A letter to a newspaper complaining about the litter in the town centre

Past: _____

Present: _____

Future: _____

Recount

Text plan: Newspaper report about a house fire

1 Orientation – this is the information that helps the reader to understand the recount (who, where, when and why).

Introduce the fire saying where and when it happened, who was involved and what may have caused it.

2 Recount events in chronological order (as they happened). Break down the event clearly. Give the reader details.

1. Smoke was noticed.
2. Neighbour helped rescue child.
3. Fire brigade arrived, controlled blaze.

3 Include comments or reflection about the event.

Comments from the fire chief (on cause); quotes/reactions of neighbours.

4 Sum up by returning to some of the main points as an ending comment. Some evaluation may be appropriate.

Lucky to escape. Importance of having fire alarms fitted.

Complete this recount about a house fire in the form of a newspaper report, taking care to follow the plan. Include the sort of detail and description a newspaper reader would expect to find. Use the style of a journalist, with some reported speech and direct quotes.

Writing tasks

1 A local river broke its banks, flooding streets and houses. You are an eyewitness to these events. Write a recount for the local website describing what happened. *(Long Writing Task)*

2 A child and his/her mother both attend a pop concert. They each describe the event in their diary/blog. Write two diary/blog entries, one for the child and one for his/her mother. *(Short Writing Task)*

3 Thieves stole a valuable painting from an art gallery. You were in the gallery at the time. Write a report for the police describing what you saw. *(Short Writing Task)*

Instructions and procedures

Definition Instructions and procedures tell a reader how to do, make or play something or how to get somewhere.

Purpose To instruct.

Text plan: Making fruit kebabs

1 Goal – a statement of what is to be achieved. Tempt/draw the reader in.

How to make fruit kebabs.
Simple – takes just 10 minutes.

2 A list of materials and equipment needed. List them in the order they are required.

List ingredients, utensils and materials.

3 A step-by-step account of what has to be done to achieve the goal.

Describe each step in the process.
1.
2.
3.

4 Sometimes an evaluation or conclusion is appropriate.

Enjoy! Simple, healthy – and delicious!

Complete the instructions for making fruit kebabs using the structure above. Don't forget to write in the simple present tense and use an imperative or bossy tone. Think about your reader and include detailed factual information.

Writing tasks

1 A publisher is putting together a collection of favourite recipes to include in a new cookery book aimed at children of your age. Write a recipe to include in the cookery book. *(Long Writing Task)*

2 You are teaching your elderly neighbour how to use email. Unfortunately, they keep forgetting what to do. Write some clear instructions that they can follow independently. *(Short Writing Task)*

3 A toy manufacturer has produced a model car in kit form. Write the instructions to include in the kit explaining to the buyer what to do. *(Short Writing Task)*

Non-chronological report

Definition Non-chronological reports give a reader information about something or somewhere. They are usually about things in general (e.g. *dogs*), not one thing in particular (e.g. *my dog Daisy*). Facts about the subject are organised into paragraphs.

Purpose To give information.

Text plan: Home computers

(1) Introduce the topic with a definition (and possibly a technical classification). Make it clear what the report will be about.

Define what is meant by home computers. How long they have been around.

(2) Give a description of the subject, e.g. some of its qualities or uses.

Describe a typical home computer set-up, e.g. speakers, Internet connection.

(3) Follow with a number of paragraphs, each one presenting detailed information on a different aspect of the topic.

Look at different aspects such as Internet shopping, communicating via email, word processing, digital photos.

(4) Return to some of the main points, rounding off with a concluding statement.

Home computers are a part of everyday life. What might happen in the future?

Complete this non-chronological report about home computers, following the plan. You will need to develop each different aspect into a separate paragraph, stating the main point and then giving specific, interesting details. Try to sound like an expert on the subject.

Writing tasks

(1) Write a report for *Living Magazine* on the 'Eco-Friendly Home'. Describe different ways in which the home is adapted to save power and water, and produce less waste. *(Long Writing Task)*

(2) Your school is deciding how to develop its grounds. Write a report for the head teacher and governors on the current state of the school grounds and how they are being used. *(Long Writing Task)*

(3) A geography website collects information about villages, towns and cities all over the world. Organise information about where you live into a report for the website. Include information on location, jobs, leisure facilities, services, transport links, etc. *(Long Writing Task)*

(4) You have been testing a new breakfast cereal. Write an evaluative report for the manufacturer saying what you thought about the product. Your report should cover taste and texture, ingredients and nutrition, packaging and appeal. *(Short Writing Task)*

Explanation

Definition An explanation tells the reader how or why something works or happens. It can be about natural things (e.g. *why volcanoes erupt*), or about mechanical things (e.g. *how a telephone works*).

Purpose To explain.

Text plan: How does water reach our taps?

Taps provide clean water to all our homes.

(1) Start with a clear and precise definition of the topic. Use the simple present tense.

(2) Describe the parts.

Taps – joined to pipes – connect to the main water supply.

(3) Describe how or why it happens in a step-by-step, logical way.

Explain each stage clearly, e.g. reservoirs, water treatment. Make clear links between steps/ideas.

(4) Explain where and when it is used. Add information about any special features.

How water is used in the home. Back-up supplies in times of drought.

(5) Finish with a summing-up paragraph that completes the explanation.

We have clean water at the turn of a tap – but not all countries are this lucky.

Complete this explanation of how water reaches our taps, making sure you use (and explain if necessary) the correct technical language. Use a style that sounds like a confident expert and write in the simple present tense.

Writing tasks

(1) 'How does that work' is an (online) encyclopaedia, explaining everyday devices. Write an entry/article on torches, describing a typical torch, explaining how it works and giving other interesting information. *(Long Writing Task)*

(2) You have invented a new labour-saving gadget to help around the house. Write a letter to the owner of a shop describing your new invention, how it works and why they should sell it. *(Short Writing Task)*

(3) A nature/science website for children includes a section on 'Frequently Asked Questions'. One question is: 'Why do apples have pips?' Write an answer explaining why apples and other fruits have pips. *(Short Writing Task)*

Discussion

Definition A discussion takes an issue and gives information about it from different points of view. It may weigh the evidence and come to a conclusion, or it may leave the reader to make up their mind about how they feel about the issue.

Purpose To present opposing views about an issue.

Text plan: Should plastic carrier bags be banned completely?

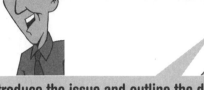

1 Start with a statement of the issue under discussion and the main viewpoints. Say why the issue is important.

Introduce the issue and outline the different views/approaches of shops and experts.

2 State the arguments FOR and give evidence to back them up. This could be more than one paragraph.

Order the main points logically:
1. Waste of natural resources
2. Add to problems of waste/litter
3. Dangerous to wildlife

3 State the evidence AGAINST and give evidence to back it up. This could be more than one paragraph.

Order the main points logically:
1. Convenient   2. Necessary
3. Can be reused

4 End with your conclusion, based on weighing up the evidence. Or refer the issue to the reader.

Decide on your conclusion, making sure it is based on evidence, or refer to the reader, e.g. *What do you think?*

Write this discussion about plastic carrier bags following the plan. Take care to present both sides of the argument in an impersonal and unbiased way. Make sure you use detail, examples, facts and evidence to support each point.

Remember you could present each argument followed by a counter-argument, e.g. the convenience of plastic carrier bags balanced against the problems of rubbish and waste; the argument about waste of natural resources countered with the idea that they can be reused.

Writing tasks

1 Your head teacher must decide whether to spend a sum of money on computers or new sports facilities. Write a balanced report for your head teacher outlining the benefits of each for the school and pupils. *(Long Writing Task)*

2 Sidley Town Council are considering opening a Skate Park. Some people think this is a great idea. Others are not happy. You are a local news reporter. Write an article covering the different points of view. *(Long Writing Task)*

3 A forum on a website has been discussing the issue: *Are footballers paid too much?* Lots of people have given their opinions – some saying yes, some saying no. Write a summary of the main points from the forum. *(Short Writing Task)*

Persuasion

Definition A persuasive text tries to make the reader think, do or buy something.

Purpose To persuade and convince the reader.

Text plan: Join the walk to school

1 Start with a clear, strong statement of the point to be argued, followed by a summary of the main arguments. Try to get the reader's attention.

Introduce the subject of walking to school rather than using the car. Appeal to the reader, e.g. *Why don't you …*

2 Each paragraph should present a point supporting the main idea with evidence and examples that will appeal to the interests/views of the reader. Paragraphs should be presented in a logical order.

Arguments for walking to school:
1. Stop traffic chaos outside the gates
2. Cut pollution
3. Good exercise
4. Fun, more time to talk to friends

3 A brief summary and clear restatement of the final point. A final appeal to the reader.

Counter any opposing arguments and end with a direct appeal.

Write an article for the school magazine persuading children and parents to join the walk to school. Follow the structure above. Take on a persuasive tone that will appeal to the reader. Sound confident and knowledgeable, and use the stylistic features of persuasive writing.

Writing tasks

1 Write a leaflet persuading people in your local area to support their local shops rather than shopping at the large out-of-town shopping centre. *(Long Writing Task)*

2 Your school's breakfast club is about to be closed down. Write a letter to Mr Hawkins, head of the local council, protesting about this and persuading him to keep it open. *(Long Writing Task)*

3 'Get Active' is a campaign to encourage children to take up a whole range of exciting activities. Write the voiceover for a TV advert encouraging children of your age to take part. *(Short Writing Task)*

4 The Golden Star Awards are about to be presented. Three of the categories are Best Sports Star, Best Friend and Best Singer. Choose someone for one of these categories and write a speech persuading the judges that he/she is definitely 'the best'. *(Short Writing Task)*

Writing fiction

This is the basic format of a narrative:

Beginning when the characters and setting are introduced	Build-up a series of events leading up to the point of the story	Problem introduce the problem	Return to the problem the problem, or event, happens	Resolution a sorting out or fixing of the problem	Ending/ Reflection by major characters or author on the events

Writing tasks

(1) A Level 5 story will include the following features:
* description
* dialogue
* action
* character reflections.

Once you have planned the narrative outline, plot these writers' techniques onto your paragraph plan to ensure a balanced story.

(2) Before you start you must decide whether you will write in the **first person** (*I, me, we*) or the **third person** (*he, she, they*).

First person Diaries, letters, autobiographies, retelling a personal experience and writing as a specific character must be in the first person.	**Third person** Many stories are written in the third person. These are generally easier to write. As narrator you know what all the characters are doing and thinking. You can skip between locations in the tale.

Once you have decided which person to write in, make sure you stick with it!

(3) You must hook your reader from the start so plan the opening sentence with care. You could choose:
* Dialogue – *'Ow ow ow,' screamed Baby Bear as he spat out the porridge. 'This is too hot to eat!'*
* Action – *Slamming the front door behind them, the three bears strode off into the forest.*
* Setting – *Early one spring morning, as the forest creatures scuttled busily about their business, three bears set off for a walk.*
* Character – *Goldilocks was a rather spoilt and very stubborn child.*
* Traditional – *Once upon a time, in the heart of a great forest, there lived three bears.*

(4) Plan the ending. This is really important, as a weak ending will ruin a good story.
* Contrast with the beginning – a frail and lonely old man from the introduction could be rosy-cheeked and smiling contentedly in the final paragraph.
* Character could reflect – *One thing is for certain, never again will I …*
* Hint at the future – *'Every last drop', those were Dad's words, 'get rid of every last drop.' But if I get rid of every last drop of potion then I'll never visit Bhalstron again.*
* Characters discuss the events – *'Do you think they are going to believe us?' Lucas asked as they rang the bell. 'Well, we'll soon find out,' Rani muttered.*

Use this page for your writer's notes and jottings of words, phrases and ideas that you can use in future story writing. Some examples have been given for you.

Character	Settings
• *a smile playing around her lips* • *tapping impatiently with her fingernails on the wooden chair arms* • *I may be old-fashioned but …*	• *dawn was creeping over the horizon* • *the chink in the curtains the only source of light* • *the gentle hum of distant traffic*
Flashback sentence starters • *Was it really only yesterday that …* • *She remembered the first time they met …* • *If only he could turn back the clock …*	**Descriptive time connectives** Level 5 writers say more than *first* or *next* and *later*. • *As the moon rose over the rooftops …* • *Almost before they realised it …* • *At that precise moment …*

Tips	★ It is not just what happens that is important, but also how the story is told. The way you tell a story can capture and keep the reader's interest. Level 5 writers must think about how their story sounds, use a style that matches the genre and purpose of their writing, and use stylistic tricks like repetition and figurative language. ★ NEVER have more than two or three important characters; you will not have time to develop them realistically. Don't waste words on minor characters – *His friends jeered menacingly* will do for the bully's friends.

Characters/character descriptions

When writing about your characters, you do not need too much description – just those details that make the character special or help to suggest the character's personality. Develop your characters through what they think, say and do, and by contrasting them with other characters. Don't say how a character feels – rather show it in their behaviour.

Shorter writing tasks
Choose one of the following tasks and write one or two paragraphs using the ideas above.

The answer section contains a checklist that will help you to see how well you did.

1 Sam, the main character in a story, is very timid and nervous. Write the opening for the story to introduce this character.

2 Old Tom lives alone and rarely goes out. One day a mysterious newcomer/person knocks on his door. Write the part of the story that describes the meeting of these two characters.

3 *I thought the room was empty. I thought I was alone. But then suddenly, to my amazement, a voice spoke my name …*

Continue this story by introducing the mysterious new character.

I could see a misty, white figer in front of Me. Goosbumps freckled on my back. I screamed. The figure then came up to me and everything became dark. I woke up staring to a girl. she gazed at me and smiled then she said "sorry for scaring you, I have been waiting for you." I asked why me. she just said " We have a mission. And your part of it. She told me this → "My name is Olivia. My Mom and dad have passed away. ~~My mother is~~ I'm always wanting to find out on new things.

Dialogue

- Use dialogue to develop your character in a way that is relevant to the plot.
- Use it instead of action to move the story along (but take care not to overuse it). Dialogue is not simply speech, it is also how characters speak.
- Vary the way you report speech. You must use adverbs and strong verbs but using too many sounds contrived; a simple 'he said' could be the best choice.
- Always make it obvious who is speaking. You must use correct speech punctuation.

Shorter writing tasks
Choose one scene from the choices below and use mainly dialogue to develop the situation.

The answer section contains a checklist that will help you to see how well you did.

(**1**) A child faces up to a school bully.

(**2**) While on a school trip, a pupil is transported back in time to Victorian times and meets a child from that period.

(**3**) Some money has been stolen from a classroom. The teacher and pupils discuss the situation and what to do.

Viewpoint – characters' reflections and narrators' comments

If you are writing a first person story from the point of view of one of the characters, bring out the voice of the character. Include their reflections on the events, their feelings, inner conflicts, any changes within themselves.

If you are writing a third person story, as a narrator outside the action describing what the characters are doing, summarise and comment on the events. You can influence the reader's view of the characters through what you describe and how.

Shorter writing tasks

Choose one scene from the choices below and develop it into one or two paragraphs. Use reflections and narrator's comments to give a clear sense of narrative viewpoint.

The answer section contains a checklist that will help you to see how well you did.

(1) Alex has mistakenly drunk a new scientific potion and is now shrinking. Continue this scene.

What was happening to me?

(2) In an empty factory, two children discover what looks like an alien spaceship. One child wants to investigate. The other wants to run away. Continue this scene.

They both peered through the murky windows.

(3) Amie has accidentally scratched Dad's new bike – his pride and joy. Her brother Joe knows she has done it and threatens to tell Dad. Write the incident from the point of view of Amie or Joe.

_____
_____
_____
_____
_____
_____
_____
_____
_____
_____
_____

Settings

Adapt your settings to the type of story you are writing, e.g. fantasy, adventure, horror, historical. When you are describing the setting of your story:
- be precise – picture the location, weather conditions and time of day
- choose place names for a purpose, e.g. to create atmosphere, expectations, humour
- gradually reveal small details, smells and sounds to bring the setting alive
- see settings through the characters' eyes; include their response as part of the description
- use settings to create tension, e.g. unexpected noises, smells, movements

Shorter writing tasks

Choose one of the following and develop it into one or two paragraphs describing what the character discovers. It is up to you to decide if the setting is realistic, fantasy, historical, science fiction ...

The answer section contains an example answer and a checklist that will help you to see how well you did.

1 *Jack peered into the underground passageway. There was no other option. Slowly, he lowered himself down ...*

2 *Gradually, the mist cleared and Ella opened her eyes.*

3 *Rather cautiously, I pushed the door open just a crack and peeked outside.*

_____

_____

_____

_____

_____

_____

_____

_____

_____

_____

_____

_____

_____

_____

_____

Adventure stories

Adventure stories are written to entertain and thrill the reader. They need lots of action and suspense. They can be written in the first or third person and need a strong narrative voice.

Planning an adventure story
You are going to write an adventure story called 'Trapped!'. Plan your story on this page and then write the story in full on your own paper.

Beginning Open with action (or dialogue leading to action). Go back – fill in details about setting (place, time) and characters.	
Build-up A series of complications to be overcome. Inform the reader of shifts in time or place. Build up sense of suspense and danger.	
Problem Make clear the central problem; there needs to be a sense of danger.	
Return to problem (climax) The characters are close to disaster. Use stylistic techniques to add pace, tension, excitement.	
Resolution The problem is solved; the main characters are safe.	
Ending/Reflection A brief reflection on the events.	

When you have finished, check your story against the Level 5 assessment points (see Answers).

Longer writing tasks
Plan and write another adventure story using one of the ideas below. Remember to create suspense and excitement to keep your reader interested.

1 *There it was again. A light flashing in the window of the building opposite ...*

This is the opening line of an adventure story. It is your task to write the rest of the story.

2 *Danger at Sea* is an anthology of adventure stories connected with the sea. The anthology is for children your age. Write a story to be included in the anthology.

Myths, legends and fables

Myths, legends and fables are all traditional stories. Myths explain natural events and how the world came to be. Legends are tales of heroic adventures. The heroes and heroines may be based on real people, but the stories are greatly exaggerated. Fables are short stories with a moral. They feature animal characters that behave like humans.

Planning a myth

You are going to write a myth to explain why rabbits have long ears. Plan your story on this page and then write your myth in full on your own paper.

Beginning Use a timeless opening, e.g. *Long, long ago* … Describe what the world was like then and how it was different to now.	
Build-up Build up the picture of this different world.	
Problem An event, a new idea, or something that brings change or conflict into the world.	
Return to problem (climax) The point just before the problem is solved. Description to heighten drama.	
Resolution Solve the problem/dispute/teach a lesson – must lead to why the rabbit has long ears.	
Ending/Reflection End with summing-up of the outcome.	

When you have finished, check your myth against the Level 5 assessment points (see Answers).

Independent writing

Plan and write myths, legends and fables based on these ideas. Remember to use story-telling techniques to engage the reader. These are all long writing tasks.

(1) Write a fable using animal characters to illustrate one of these morals:
  • *Persuasion is sometimes better than force.*
  • *Don't let greed be your downfall.*
  • *Everything that glistens is not gold.*

(2) Plan and write a legend using one of these titles:
  • Sir Ferdinand and the Dragon of Gloth
  • The Quest for the Golden Orb

Writing playscripts

A playscript is written to be performed. It can be one short scene or a complete story split into several scenes. Dialogue and stage directions move the action on and make it clear to the reader what is happening. They are also important for developing the characters and the relationships between them.

Planning a playscript

You are going to write a script for a scene called 'The Lost Kitten'. On this page, plan how the events will unfold. Then write the scene in full on your own paper. Make sure you set out the dialogue following the usual playscript layout.

Beginning Decide who the characters are (cast list) and where/when the scene takes place (setting).	
Introduce characters/problem A short exchange to introduce the characters/situation and the problem.	
Build-up Build up tension between characters. Develop the characters, e.g. contrasting speech styles.	
Return to problem Create tension, e.g. time running out, characters desperate. Stage directions to show response/feelings/movements.	
Resolution The problem is solved, e.g. by entrance of new character or revealing a 'hidden' piece of information.	
Ending Brief comment from one of the characters.	

When you have finished, check your script against the Level 5 assessment points (see Answers).

Longer writing tasks

1 Ben wants to go to the zoo on Saturday. His sister Becky wants to go to the cinema. Dad doesn't mind where they go, as long as they can finally come to a decision. Present this scene in the form of a script.

2 Class G6 are putting on a play for parents. It is based on the story of Cinderella. They need the script for the scene where the ugly sisters receive their invitation to the ball – and Cinderella does not. Help them to write it.

Grammar

Level 5 writers should use a variety of sentences in their writing. They must be able to:

- vary the length of their sentences, using simple, compound and complex sentences
- write complex sentences with subordinate clauses at the start, middle and end of the sentence
- use different types of sentence (questions, commands, exclamations) if appropriate
- vary the order of words and clauses to change the focus of the sentence

> **Tip** In longer sentences you may need to use commas to separate phrases or clauses.

1 Follow this longer sentence with a short simple sentence for impact.

She searched through the cases, frantically throwing the neatly packed clothes onto a heap on the floor.

_____

2 Follow this longer sentence with a short sentence to make an idea stand out.

Last year, many of our Year 6 children had an opportunity to attend the Centre and try out the activities.

_____

3 Follow this sentence with a complex sentence that conveys more than one idea or piece of information economically.

The Earth travels round the Sun.

_____

4 Follow this sentence with a complex sentence that shows the relationship between the two characters.

Tyler was waiting for Harry.

_____

5 Add a clause into the middle of this sentence to give a short piece of information succinctly.

The door _____ was now closed.

6 Add a subordinate clause to the end of this sentence to develop the point.

The library will look much better _____

7 Add a subordinate clause to the start of this sentence that clarifies the point.

_____ _____ *many people did seem to enjoy the show.*

8 Reorder this sentence so the main focus comes at the end.

There was Mr Atkins standing in the doorway.

_____

Try these short writing tasks. Focus on using a variety of sentences.

9 *Jess was alone in the house. She heard a noise outside.*

Write this idea as a paragraph for a story. Use a variety of sentences to build up suspense/tension.

_____

_____

_____

_____

10 Write a short encyclopaedia entry about squirrels. Use a variety of sentences to make your writing sound interesting and to present information clearly and concisely.

_____

_____

_____

_____

11 Alex has won the school's talent contest. Write Alex's diary/blog for that day. Use a variety of sentence types to show the writer's excitement and to make it sound like a real diary/blog.

_____

_____

_____

_____

12 Write a short flier to persuade people to give unwanted items to your charity collection. Use a range of sentence types to create impact and appeal to the reader.

_____

_____

_____

_____

Paragraphs

Paragraphs are used to structure the main ideas in your writing. Each paragraph should have a clear focus and they should link together to form your text. Level 5 writers should be able to clearly signal the links between paragraphs to the reader.

Here is a paragraph plan for a report evaluating a new computer game. Add an opening phrase for each paragraph to introduce/make the focus clear.

Introduction

> *I am writing to …*

Good graphics

Simple to follow (not too complicated)

Doesn't keep your attention enough

Quality of audio is poor

Conclusion

Writing a paragraph

You must also sequence and link your ideas within each paragraph. A range of devices can help you to do this, e.g. pronouns, connectives, phrases that refer back to text (*This is where …, etc.*).

Here is the start of a paragraph describing a possible location for a new supermarket. Continue the paragraph, sequencing and linking the ideas.

The next possibility is Stempford. This is a small town ten miles from Oakley. It has …

_____

_____

_____

_____

_____

_____

_____

_____

_____

ACHIEVE LEVEL 5

ENGLISH

Answers for Practice Questions

Page 8 – Writing non-fiction – Practising non-fiction text features – The passive voice in impersonal writing

Example answers:

1. The workshop will be held in the school hall. A range of practical activities has been planned for the afternoon. All the books and materials will be provided.

2. Whales are hunted for use in scientific research. They are also hunted for meat. Several hundred whales can be taken in a season. This is wrong.

3. Unwanted clothing is collected and put into bags. Next the clothes are sorted and separated into different boxes. Finally the boxes are taken to the charity shop.

4. Food poisoning can be avoided by following basic hygiene rules. These rules are displayed in the kitchen area.

Page 9 – Writing non-fiction – Practising non-fiction text features – Using the right voice – formal and informal

Example answers:

1. The sand spider varies in size from just a few millimetres to a maximum of 3 cm across. It burrows down in the sand and remains hidden, waiting for an unwary insect to become its prey. A sand spider's bite is potentially fatal.

2. The closure of the local post office has caused considerable debate. The campaign against the closure has been well publicised and villagers remain hopeful that the council will reconsider their decision.

3. We propose installing security lighting to deter vandals. All the work will be undertaken with adult supervision.

4. Polar bears have thick fur to keep them well insulated against the icy winds. The yellowy-white colour of their coats provides them good camouflage in the Arctic ice flows.

Page 10 – Writing non-fiction – Practising non-fiction text features – Tense

Example answers:

1. Past: Every day just before home time, we used to sit at our desks and listen intently as Mrs Wilson read a chapter from the latest story.
   Present: When I visit schools today I am amazed at the equipment in classrooms.
   Future: Perhaps one day I will use Mrs Wilson as a character in a story.

2. Past: The museum was first opened in 2001.
   Present: There are now over 20 buildings for you to see.
   Future: We will be adding more buildings in the next 12 months.

3. Past: Fifty years ago, many people cycled to work and school.
   Present: There is so much traffic on roads today that cycling is dangerous.
   Future: Special cycle routes will encourage more people to cycle.

4. Past: I was horrified to see that all the litterbins had been vandalised.
   Present: It seems people just throw their litter on the floor.
   Future: I hope the council will take this matter seriously in their next meeting.

Pages 11–16 – Writing non-fiction

Own answers to Short and Long Writing Tasks.

Page 19 – Writing fiction – Characters/character descriptions

A Level 5 answer should contain the following features:

- descriptive details of appearance that make the character distinctive, e.g. *pale, freckly face*
- the character is developed through actions/behaviour, e.g. backing away from a situation to show timidity
- contrasts with other characters, e.g. grumpiness of one character with chattiness of another
- use of speech to show more of the character, e.g. *'If you must,' mumbled Old Tom*
- the character's feelings are shown rather than told, e.g. *his hands were shaking now*
- the reactions of others to the character

Page 20 – Writing fiction – Dialogue

A Level 5 answer should contain the following features:

- variety in the reporting clause – some use of *said*, some speech verbs (*whispered, groaned*), some use of adverbs (*carefully, angrily*)
- dialogue that moves narrative along, e.g. *'Would you like to come and see where I work?'*
- dialogue that develops character, e.g. *'Not scared, are you?' smirked Angela*
- make it obvious who is speaking
- use of correct speech punctuation (see page 32 for help with this)
- new paragraph started for each new speaker

Page 21 – Writing fiction – Viewpoint – characters' reflections and narrators' comments

A Level 5 answer should contain the following features:

- details that portray the personality of the characters
- comments on the action
- the thoughts and feelings of the characters
- in a third person narrative, the events shown from more than one point of view
- in a first person narrative, represent the voice of the character, e.g. asides to the reader

Page 22 – Writing fiction – Settings

This is an example answer for question 1 (the traditional tale):

Long, long ago in a far away village there lived a young man by the name of Jack. Now, Jack was the youngest of three sons and – well, to tell you the truth – Jack was a little bit lazy. In fact, he was as lazy as a cat asleep on a summer's day.

Each of Jack's brothers had left home to seek his fortune – and now it was Jack's turn. So off he went down the twisting, winding road away from the village and into the forest – the deep, dark forest. The deep, dark forest where the trees whispered the names of travellers.

Note: traditional story opening; use of repetition (*deep, dark forest*); oral story-telling techniques; natural conversational style (*Now ...*); speaking to the reader (*to tell you the truth*).

A Level 5 answer should contain the following features:
- details that help the reader picture the scene, e.g. *water trickled down the walls*
- details that suggest the genre of story, e.g. *women in crinoline skirts*
- use of all the senses, e.g. *the buzz of machinery, the icy bite of the water*
- setting and character's behaviour linked, e.g. character's reaction shows bravery or fear
- vocabulary used to build up mood, e.g. *cold metal*
- a variety of sentence types to create an appropriate mood, e.g. a question to build suspense
- use of similes, metaphors, alliteration or patterning

Page 23 – Writing fiction – Adventure stories
Use these Level 5 assessment points to help you check your adventure story:
- start the story in an exciting way, e.g. using action
- develop the main characters, e.g. make one brave, one fearful
- include dialogue and description as well as action
- use paragraphs to separate events/key parts of the story
- make clear shifts in time, location, focus
- include an ending that completes the overall shape of the story, e.g. referring back to something
- use details of the setting to build up mood, sense of danger
- deliberately change pace or mood, e.g. descriptive paragraph to slow/build up tension; sudden surprising action
- engage the reader, e.g. questions, direct address
- use vocabulary for effect
- comment on the action; show the thoughts of the characters

Page 24 – Writing fiction – Myths, legends and fables
Use these Level 5 assessment points to help you check your myth:
- follow the myth structure – beginning, build-up, problem, return to problem, resolution, ending
- use a traditional story-telling style, e.g. old-fashioned vocabulary, typical opening (*Long, long ago when the Earth was young ...*)
- use paragraphs to separate main events
- use chronological and descriptive time connectives, e.g. *As days went by, At that precise moment*
- develop good and bad characters and contrast them, e.g. *Rabbit ran towards his burrow. The evil fox chased after him, snarling fiercely.*
- use rich description to draw the reader in and heighten key moments

- use story-telling techniques to engage the reader, e.g. patterned language
- include dialogue to show character and to take the story forward
- comment/reflect on the actions; show feelings of the characters

Page 25 – Writing fiction – Writing playscripts
Use these Level 5 assessment points to help you check your playscript:
- follow the plan so the scene develops and moves on with a sense of purpose
- use dialogue to move the action on and make it clear to the reader what is going on, e.g. **Sam:** *What are you doing with that kitten?*
- make sure there is a satisfying resolution
- include brief scene-setting notes to keep the reader informed (if necessary split events into separate scenes to mark changes in time, place)
- set out dialogue using the usual script layout
- use contrasting speech styles for different characters, e.g. **Mrs Brown:** *Oh, you dear children ...*
- use dialogue and stage directions to develop lively characters and the relationships between them, e.g. **Nick:** *Well come on then, Brains – what's your idea?*
- make the dialogue sound natural, e.g. shortened forms (*We've*), ellipses (*...*)
- include stage directions to show characters' actions, reactions and movements (e.g. *Sam looks surprised*) as well as how lines should be spoken (*anxiously*)

Pages 26–27 – Grammar – Sentences
Example answers:
1. The key was not there.
2. This was a great success.
3. Without the Sun, life as we know it would not be possible as it is our only source of light and heat.
4. As the younger boy approached nervously, Tyler slipped from the wall and stood deliberately blocking his path.
5. The door, which had been open, was now closed.
6. The library will look much better when the painting has been completed.
7. Despite the problems with the stage, many people did seem to enjoy the show.
8. There, standing in the doorway, was Mr Atkins.
9. *Have you used ... ?*
   Short sentences for impact; questions to draw the reader in; complex sentences, e.g. to relate the characters' feelings to events; repetition; sentences starting with adverbs (e.g. *Slowly ...*) or subordinate clauses; variation in word order to delay focus.
10. *Have you used ... ?*
   Complex sentences to explain, contrast ideas; an occasional simple sentence, e.g. *The Red squirrel is native to Britain*; a subordinate clause embedded into the middle of a sentence: *The grey squirrel, which is commonly found in gardens, ...* ; a variety of connectives in your sentences, e.g. *Although, but, because, if*; a passive construction to focus on squirrels, e.g. *Squirrels are sometimes ...*
11. *Have you used ... ?*

Questions and commands to indicate conversational language; some long complex sentences with several subordinate clauses, e.g. *Just as I was about to go on stage, they had to stop the show because it was too hot in the hall and everyone was feeling ill*; short sentences for effect; variation in word order for emphasis/to change the focus of sentences.

12. *Have you used … ?*

Questions and imperatives; passives to shift sentence focus; short sentences, e.g. *Please help*; a sentence that starts with a subordinate clause, e.g. *Unless we do something …*; varied word order to bring an idea to the fore.

Page 28 – Grammar – Paragraphs

Example of paragraph openings:

I am writing to …
My first impressions …
Another good feature …
However …
I would also like to bring to your attention …
In conclusion …
Overall …

The following phrases might help you to develop and link ideas:

In the town centre …
On the edge of the town there is a large site …
This is where …
One of the best reasons for choosing this site is …
Although … , it is also …
However …

Page 29 – Grammar – Connectives

Possible connectives are:

1. Therefore, As a result,
2. On the other hand,
3. Meanwhile
4. Moreover,
5. For example,
6. Two years later
7. Instead
8. Yet, However,
9. Furthermore,
10. Almost immediately

Page 30 – Grammar – Connectives

Example connectives/sentences:

1. … as they can be very high in sugar and fats.
2. … because it would be dangerous.
3. … when it is dark and weather conditions are bad.
4. … if/as long as everything goes according to plan.
5. … otherwise it will be too late/before it is too late.
6. … despite the lack of funds.
7. Maria crossed the market place and hurried down the alleyway, although none of the villagers seemed to notice her.
8. The leaves, which were shaped like hands, moved slowly in the breeze, as if they were waving.
9. As the soldiers approached, Megan tried the door, even though she knew it would be locked.
10. There was nothing special about Matthew, except for his eyes, which twinkled when he thought of something funny.
11. When he returned home many years later, the Prince had changed because of his adventures.

12. There was once a king who spent all his time counting his money while his people starved.

Page 31 – Punctuation – Separating clauses and sentences

1. *Many, many centuries ago there lived a one-eyed giant called Casper. He lived in a dark, damp, dreary cave high up in the mountains. Although he was quite alone, Casper was perfectly happy. After all, he knew nothing else.*

   But then one day, just after he had finished his breakfast, Casper heard a clopping sound coming up the side of the mountain. It seemed to be coming nearer and nearer. Then suddenly, much to Casper's surprise, appearing over the mountain ridge came a man on horseback. Casper, who had never seen a man before, jumped to his feet, causing the ground to vibrate violently and the man to fall from his horse. Clutching his sword, the terrified man leapt to his feet.

2. *Did you know that the average family in Britain throws away six trees' worth of paper every year? Six trees! Think about that. That's not to mention all the tin cans, bottles, food, clothes and everything else we put in our bins.*

   All the rubbish collected from our homes is dumped in landfill sites or burned in incinerators, creating harmful gases that pollute our environment. Moreover, some of the waste, like plastic bottles and nappies, doesn't rot away and just stays around for ages. Yuk!

   So, what can we do about it? Well, the answer is to reuse, reduce and recycle* your rubbish. Whether it's reducing what you throw away, reusing resources or recycling more, you can do your bit. Why not begin today?

   * could use capital letters for emphasis

Page 32 – Punctuation – Speech punctuation

Example answer:

'Lucy Megson, what do you have there?' demanded Mrs Jackson, peering over her glasses.
'It's … it's … ' stuttered Lucy, unable to think of a suitable answer.
'I hope it's not a mobile phone. You know mobile phones are not allowed in school, don't you?' warned Mrs Jackson.
'No, it's not a mobile phone. I'm not sure what it is, Mrs Jackson. I found it in the playground and it keeps bleeping at me and …'
'Bleeping!' exclaimed Mrs Jackson. 'Bring it here, Lucy, at once.'

Page 32 – Punctuation – Punctuating a playscript

Ross: We have to take it back. It doesn't belong to us. Can't you see that, Ellie?
Ellie: No, Ross. I can't! I was the one who found it. I was the one who picked it up. I was the one who …
Ross: I know that, Ellie, but …
Ellie: Don't 'but' me, Ross Jameson!

Page 33 – Punctuation – Dashes and brackets

Example answers:

1. *What a day! I am never going out in public with my parents again – never! My mother (as always) never stopped talking for one second. (Is this normal?) Dad*

– *as I guessed he would – hid himself in the newspaper all day.*

2. *Mr Higgins was one of those people you just don't want to annoy – you know the sort? When he was angry (which was most of the time) everyone knew about it.*

3. *Everyone was in fancy dress apart from me – honestly, I'm not joking. Ellie was dressed as a fairy (all in pink!), Robbie was an alien (there's a surprise) and Katie was an elephant – well, that's what she said.*

4. *There is no time to waste – we must act now. These people have just one bucket (5 litres) of water a day. Your money can transform their lives – and give them a future.*

Page 34 – Punctuation – Semi-colons

1. The finishing line was in sight; victory was a possibility.
2. This was our last chance; the gateway was almost closed.
3. We waited in silence; Mrs Jenkins was in no mood for chatter.
4. The receptionist was not there; I was quite alone.
5. Some animals will survive these changes in climate; others will not.
6. Reports seem to have been exaggerated; no one was hurt.
7. Crops have failed throughout the country; people are starving.
8. He was born a penniless orphan; he died a millionaire.

Page 35 – Punctuation – Writing lists

1. A table appeared before Dylan's eyes, covered with all the food he had wished for: chocolate cake, strawberries, pizza, flap jacks, bowls of crisps, ice cream and thick banana milk shakes.
2. The shop will sell a variety of healthy snacks: fruit, carrot sticks, muesli bars, bags of nuts and raisins.
3. Future Park has many fascinating attractions: a water dome heated entirely by solar power; sculptures made from recycled materials; a wind-powered fairground and a totally organic garden.
4. The kennels were full of dogs, dogs of all shapes and sizes: Dalmatians, Alsatians, terriers, retrievers, poodles and spaniels, greyhounds and basset hounds.
5. It is important to eat a balanced diet: carbohydrates, which give you energy; proteins to help growth; fibre to aid digestion and some fats to act as an energy store.

Page 36 – Vocabulary – Choosing words for effect – Nouns and verbs

Here are some examples. Your sentences may be completely different. It depends on your choice of verbs and nouns.

1. Mrs Wilson hurried along Church Street clutching a carrier bag.
2. A Ferrari slid to a halt outside the arena. There was a blast of heavy metal as the electronic door buzzed open.
3. In the gloom, Eric trudged across the playing field, huddled in his sweatshirt. It began to drizzle.

4. Professor Jenkins blundered into the laboratory, clutching the test tube. He began to search for the notebook.

Page 36 – Vocabulary – Choosing words for effect – Adding adjectives/extended noun phrases

Examples of possible adjectives: soft, gentle moonlight/sinister, shadowy moonlight; flickering, welcoming flames/fierce, raging flames; a trickle of sparkling water/brown, swirling water; sunlit garden/overgrown, tangled garden

Page 37 – Vocabulary – Choosing words for effect – Adverbs

Examples of possible adverbs: shuffled uncomfortably/ restlessly; waited patiently/anxiously; stared nervously/in amazement/warily; knocked urgently/politely; stood bravely/proudly; balanced nimbly/clumsily

Page 37 – Vocabulary – Choosing words for effect – Words for purpose and effect

1. *His eyes narrowed as he peered at his new victim. A cruel smirk flickered on his thin lips.*
2. *The four walls of the vast library were lined from floor to ceiling with shelves of ancient books. In the centre of the room, figures huddled at carved desks, reading dusty manuscripts.*
3. *Every step she took seemed to echo in the deadly silence. Low-hanging branches brushed her face. Her skin crawled and her spine tingled in fear.*

Page 38 – Vocabulary – Figurative language – Simile

Examples of similes:

1. Leaves like an elephant's ears; flower petals like tissue paper
2. Eyes like twinkling stars; a smile like a summer's day
3. Ran like a startled gazelle

Page 38 – Vocabulary – Figurative language – Metaphor

Examples of sentences using the metaphors:

1. Suddenly the room was filled with a swirling kaleidoscope of colours, making my head spin.
2. His feet sank into the thick carpet of grass.
3. The cave was a giant gaping mouth, waiting to swallow up anyone who dared to enter.

Page 39 – Vocabulary – Figurative language – Personification

Example answers: windows stared blankly; darkness wrapped itself tightly; the wind whispered soothingly; leaves tumbled madly; the machine awoke suddenly; the television slept undisturbed; winter gently touched the world; sunlight softly touched

Page 39 – Vocabulary – Figurative language – Alliteration

Example answers:

1. The sea soothed the soft sand.
    A carriage clanked and clattered over the cobbles.

The wind whisked and whispered its way through the tree.

2. Don't waste water – be water wise.
   Pablo's Pizza – perfection on a plate.

Page 40 – Spelling – Spelling rules – Plurals

1. families	2. shelves
3. discos	4. journeys
5. attempts	6. potatoes
7. patches	8. stripes
9. taxes	10. nappies

Page 40 – Spelling – Spelling rules – Verb endings

died dying dies; tackled tackling tackles; extended extending extends; travelled travelling travels; replied replying replies; fluttered fluttering flutters; surveyed surveying surveys; realised realising realises; gossiped gossiping gossips; studied studying studies; controlled controlling controls; valued valuing values

Page 41 – Spelling – Spelling rules – Root words, prefixes and suffixes

nastiest novelist cleverest emptier trickier speechless shameful pitiful forgetful actually stubby murky perfectly scaly hungrily unlikely originally heavily shakily edible valuable reversible demonstration attention extension misplace illegal admire impolite dissatisfied already Internet microscope bicycle automatic

Pages 46–47 – Reading comprehension – Falcon Fun Days

1. Birds of prey book and a badge.
2. Phone.
3. '…giving a real insight into their behaviour in the wild…'
4. One from: To persuade people to go; children may see the pictures and ask parents if they can they go.
5. Yes; No; Yes; Yes.
6. An expression 'WOW – it was amazing' and then an explanation using some facts about the birds/treats/lunch. Or 'Oh my goodness – it was awful/scary' with an explanation using some facts about the birds, treats or lunch.
7. To add authenticity (real people who were there); to give viewpoints of people who have been before; to provide extra details about the experience. (1 mark each)

Pages 48–49 – Reading comprehension – Interview with Darren Shan

1. Because that's how long it will take to tell the story.
2. That was quite fun as well, but it was also quite horrific.
3. Braver and tougher.
4. For each of the following reasons 1 mark: The questions are separated which helps us to choose which ones we want to read; we can skim and scan the text until we reach the question we are interested in.
5. Any two of the following reasons (1 mark each): Wants children to know what Darren Shan is like; this way he can tell lots of children the same information at the same time; to publicise his books; to attract more readers and fans; to make more money.

6. Any three from: The more you write the better you will become; perseverance, hard work, a lot of time; self-belief.

Pages 50–51 – Reading comprehension – Pride and Prejudice

1. Mrs Long.
2. (Mr) Bingley.
3. 'This was invitation enough.'
4. Any two from the following (1 mark for each reason): That he is busy doing something; he is not interested in the conversation; he is used to Mrs Bennet talking to him even when he doesn't answer.
5. She is a real chatterbox. (1 mark) A second mark awarded for an example from the text or expansion of the above, e.g.: once she starts talking she doesn't stop/she is talking so fast that she doesn't even stop for a breath.
6. Any of the following (1 mark for identifying an example from the text and 1 mark for explanation):
   He ignores her – 'Mr Bennet made no answer.'
   He asks if Bingley is married or single – he knows this will excite her.
   He acts daft saying 'how can it affect them?' as he knows his wife is obsessed with marrying off his children.
   At the end he says 'Mr Bingley might like you the best of the party' teasing her that Mr Bingley might prefer her to her daughters.
7. Mrs Bennet calls her husband Mr Bennet.
   Bingley earns between four and five thousand a year.
   Bingley arrives in a chaise and four.

Pages 52–53 – Reading comprehension – First day at school

1. Uniform.
2. To emphasise how far away the child feels on their first day at school; to use language that a small child might use.
3. The railings protect the school.
   The railings stop children from escaping.
4. Roger McGough uses limited punctuation to illustrate that a small child is speaking or to show the child is talking without taking a breath. (1 mark)
   The disjointed sentences demonstrate that the child is upset and confused or this style of writing creates the image that the child is distressed and saying whatever comes into their head. (1 mark)
5. Teachers often use books to start discussions as many children in reception classes might feel like the child in the poem. (1 mark) To cheer children up who feel the same as the child in the poem. (1 mark)

Tea-cher. The one who makes the tea.	To show the child's misunderstanding of some words.
I wish she was here.	To describe how alone the child feels.
And the railings. All around the railings	To emphasise how trapped and frightened the child is.

Page 54–55 – Reading comprehension –
Seasick

1. The squid.
2. Any four from: whelk, whale, squid, sole, octopus, mussels, hake, salmon, mermaid, rays, herring, porpoise, oyster, urchin, plaice, eel, whiting, sturgeon, dace, brill, cod. *(1 mark for two correct; 2 marks for four correct)*
3. When this is read aloud the listener would not see the play on words so it is not as effective as when reading. The performer would stress the names of the sea creatures when read aloud. *(2 marks for either detailed answer or 2 marks for both reasons without expansion)*
4. Any three of the following ideas *(1 mark each)*: jumping around, puppets, different voices, pausing after humorous lines.
5. doctopus – doctor
   orcwardly – awkwardly
   sick squid – £6

Connectives

Connectives link different parts of the text together. They can link paragraphs, sentences or clauses within a sentence. Connectives give the writing structure and organisation, and help the reader to follow your thoughts.

Connectives can show time (e.g. *meanwhile, eventually*), order (e.g. *firstly, in addition*), contrast (e.g. *on the other hand, alternatively*), addition or reinforcement (e.g. *moreover, furthermore*), causes and effects (e.g. *because, as a result, therefore*).

Level 5 writers should be able to use a wide range of connectives to link thoughts and ideas.

Use appropriate connectives to link these sentences. Sometimes there might be more than one possibility.

1 There have been some incidents of vandalism. [   ] the garden will be closed after 6 p.m.

2 It may be true that school uniform is not that attractive. [   ] people often say a class of children in school uniform looks very smart.

3 Ben was racing towards the finishing line. [   ] Ryan sat in the shade of the tree, his eyes closing in the midday sun.

4 Turning lights off when you leave the room helps save electricity. [   ] it saves money too.

5 There are many different forms of poetry. [   ] there are haikus, limericks, ballads and shape poems.

6 The first unmanned mission will be in 2012. [   ] a robot will be sent on a further exploration.

7 Don't wrap your lunch in a plastic bag. [   ] go for a reusable container.

8 We spend hundreds of pounds a year getting rid of rubbish. [   ] we could easily cut that amount in half.

9 Fruit contains a wide range of vitamins to keep the body healthy. [   ] it is low in fat and low in calories.

10 Small tremors were noticed at about 12.15. [   ] the volcano erupted.

Level 5 writers should also use a variety of connectives to form complex sentences.

Add an appropriate connective and continue the ideas in these sentences from non-fiction texts. Use a different connective each time.

1 Fruit is a healthier alternative to cakes and biscuits _____

_____

2 Rollerblading is not permitted in the playground _____

_____

3 There are more road accidents in winter _____

4 The explorers expect to reach the North Pole some time next week _____

_____

5 We need your help now _____

6 The swimming club continues to grow _____

Use connectives to rewrite these simple sentences from stories as complex sentences that link a number of ideas.

7 Maria crossed the market place. _____

8 The leaves moved slowly in the breeze. _____

9 Megan tried the door. _____

10 There was nothing special about Matthew. _____

11 The Prince had changed. _____

12 There was once a king. _____

Punctuation

SEPARATING SENTENCES AND CLAUSES

If you are aiming to achieve Level 5, you will already know the basics of sentence punctuation and be using capital letters, full stops, question marks, exclamation marks and some commas accurately.

To achieve Level 5, you need to make sure you can use commas not only to separate items in a list, but also to separate phrases and clauses within longer complex sentences.

(1) Put the full stops, capital letters and commas into this passage of narrative writing.

many many centuries ago there lived a one-eyed giant called casper he lived in a dark damp dreary cave high up in the mountains although he was quite alone casper was perfectly happy after all he knew nothing else

but then one day just after he had finished his breakfast casper heard a clopping sound coming up the side of the mountain it seemed to be coming nearer and nearer then suddenly much to casper's surprise appearing over the mountain ridge came a man on horseback casper who had never seen a man before jumped to his feet causing the ground to vibrate violently and the man to fall from his horse clutching his sword the terrified man leapt to his feet

(2) Put the sentence punctuation (capital letters, full stops, question marks, exclamation marks) and commas into this passage of non-narrative writing.

did you know that the average family in britain throws away six trees' worth of paper every year six trees think about that that's not to mention all the tin cans bottles food clothes and everything else we put in our bins

all the rubbish collected from our homes is dumped in landfill sites or burned in incinerators creating harmful gases that pollute our environment moreover some of the waste like plastic bottles and nappies doesn't rot away and just stays around for ages yuk

so what can we do about it well the answer is to reuse reduce and recycle your rubbish whether it's reducing what you throw away reusing resources or recycling more you can do your bit why not begin today

Speech punctuation

When you use direct speech, make sure it is fully punctuated. This means remembering to use full stops, commas and question marks as well as speech marks (e.g *'I'm over here,' said Nicky.*)

Two other forms of punctuation are useful to make a character's speech sound realistic:
* apostrophes in shortened forms (e.g. *I'm, we'll*) make direct speech sound natural.
* the occasional ellipsis (…) is useful to show a character's speech has been cut short, or their voice has trailed away …

Here is the start of a piece of dialogue. Put in the missing punctuation. Then continue the dialogue to show how it might develop. *(Short Writing Task)*

Lucy Megson what do you have there demanded Mrs Jackson peering over her glasses

Its its stuttered Lucy unable to think of a suitable answer

_____

_____

_____

_____

_____

_____

PUNCTUATING A PLAYSCRIPT

A playscript does not use speech marks but other punctuation helps to tell the actors how to read the lines – when to pause, what to stress, what is questioned, what is exclaimed.

Here is the start of a scene from a playscript. Put in the missing punctuation. Continue the scene to show how it might develop. *(Short Writing Task)*

Ross: We have to take it back it doesnt belong to us cant you see that Ellie

Ellie: No Ross I can t I was the one who found it I was the one who picked it up I was the one who

Ross: I know that Ellie but

_____

_____

_____

_____

_____

_____

_____

| Tip | ★ **Warning: Do not overuse ellipses as this could spoil the effect.** |

Using dashes and brackets

Dashes (–) are often used in informal writing to add asides or afterthoughts.

Brackets ( ) can be used in a similar way. They are sometimes used in more formal writing to add a further explanation or a definition.

1 Rewrite this diary entry using brackets and dashes to add some comments or asides that give an impression of the writer's thoughts and reflections. *(Short Writing Task)*

What a day! I am never going out in public with my parents again. My mother never stopped talking for one second. Dad hid himself in the newspaper all day.

_____

_____

_____

_____

2 Rewrite this story opening using brackets and dashes to add comments and asides aimed at the reader. *(Short Writing Task)*

Mr Higgins was one of those people you just don't want to annoy. When he was angry everyone knew about it.

_____

_____

_____

_____

3 Rewrite this informal letter using brackets and dashes to add some comments and asides to make it sound chatty and humorous. *(Short Writing Task)*

Everyone was in fancy dress apart from me. Ellie was dressed as a fairy, Robbie was an alien and Katie was an elephant.

_____

_____

_____

_____

4 Use brackets and dashes to add persuasive comments and factual information to this leaflet. *(Short Writing Task)*

There is no time to waste. These people have just one bucket of water a day. Your money can transform their lives.

_____

_____

_____

_____

Semi-colons

Semi-colons can be used in place of connectives to join two closely related clauses. Using a semi-colon can be effective because it makes a direct link between the two ideas.

Replace the connective in these sentences with a semi-colon. Read both sentences and decide which is the most effective.

(1) The finishing line was in sight and victory was a possibility.

_____

(2) This was our last chance as the gateway was almost closed.

_____

(3) We waited in silence because Mrs Jenkins was in no mood for chatter.

_____

(4) The receptionist was not there so I was quite alone.

_____

(5) Some animals will survive these changes in climate while others will not.

_____

(6) Reports seem to have been exaggerated as no one was hurt.

_____

(7) Crops have failed throughout the country which means people are starving.

_____

(8) He was born a penniless orphan but when he died he was a millionaire.

_____

Writing lists

To achieve Level 5, you must be able to use colons, semi-colons and commas in a list.

The rules are:
- use a colon to introduce a list
- use commas to separate single items in a list
- use semi-colons to separate phrases or clauses in a list

Punctuate these list sentences.

1 A table appeared before Dylan's eyes covered with all the food he had wished for chocolate cake strawberries pizza flap jacks bowls of crisps ice cream and thick banana milk shakes.

_____

_____

_____

2 The shop will sell a variety of healthy snacks fruit carrot sticks muesli bars bags of nuts and raisins.

_____

_____

_____

3 Future Park has many fascinating attractions a water dome heated entirely by solar power sculptures made from recycled materials a wind-powered fairground and a totally organic garden.

_____

_____

_____

4 The kennels were full of dogs dogs of all shapes and sizes Dalmatians Alsatians terriers retrievers poodles and spaniels greyhounds and basset hounds.

_____

_____

_____

5 It is important to eat a balanced diet carbohydrates which give you energy proteins to help growth fibre to aid digestion and some fats to act as an energy store.

_____

_____

_____

Choosing words for effect

Level 5 writers choose words with care. The secret is thinking about the effect you want to create and choosing the best words to create this effect.

Be adventurous! Choose exciting, imaginative, bold words rather than words you use every day.

Nouns and verbs

Precise nouns and powerful verbs help to make your writing effective.

Rewrite these sentences improving the verbs and nouns to create clear, interesting pictures for the reader.

(1) The lady walked along the street carrying a bag.

_____

(2) A car pulled up outside the building. There was the sound of music as the door opened.

_____

_____

(3) In the dark the boy walked across the grass, dressed in a top. It began to rain.

_____

(4) The man went into the room, holding the object in his hand. He began to look for the book.

_____

_____

Adding adjectives/extended noun phrases

Adjectives are used to add something new to a noun. They can create different moods and feelings, e.g. *a severe look* is quite different to *an encouraging look*.

Add adjectives (or an adjective phrase) to the nouns in the first column to create a happy mood and in the second column to create a menacing mood.

[ ]	moonlight	[ ]	moonlight
[ ]	flames	[ ]	flames
[ ]	water	[ ]	water
[ ]	garden	[ ]	garden

Adverbs

Adverbs refine the meaning of verbs, e.g. *he walked slowly/swiftly/awkwardly/ regularly/everywhere*. Sometimes a phrase acts as an adverb, e.g. *sobbed as if her heart would break*.

Never use adverbs that mean the same as the verb, e.g. *raced quickly*.

Use an adverb to say something different about the verb in each column.

shuffled		shuffled	
waited		waited	
stared		stared	
knocked		knocked	
stood		stood	
balanced		balanced	

Words for purpose and effect

1. Write the next two or three sentences for this story. Choose words that make the reader feel wary of this character.

   The shopkeeper was standing behind the counter.

   _____

   _____

   _____

2. Write the next two or three sentences for this story. Choose words to create a clear picture for the reader.

   Slowly the door swung open.

   _____

   _____

   _____

3. Write the next two or three sentences for this story. Choose words to create a feeling of unease and tension.

   It was dark in the forest.

   _____

   _____

   _____

Figurative language

Level 5 writers use figurative language (similes, metaphors, personification) and sound patterns (alliteration, repetition) to make their writing effective.

Simile

A simile creates a sharp description using very few words. It makes a comparison with something else using the words *like* or *as*.

> **Example:** *Heat – like a devil's furnace*

Write similes you might use to describe the following.

1 A plant that no one has seen before

_____

2 A smiling face

_____

3 Someone running away from danger

_____

Metaphor

A metaphor does not use the words *like* or *as*. It creates a description by saying something is something else. It is a very powerful descriptive tool.

> **Example**: *The fog was like a blanket* (simile)
> *The fog was a blanket* OR *The blanket of fog* (metaphors)

Change these similes into metaphors and use them in a descriptive sentence.

1 Colours like in a kaleidoscope

_____

2 The grass was like a thick carpet

_____

3 The cave was like a giant mouth

_____

Personification

Some metaphors make objects sound like they are human. When we give human characteristics to a 'non-human' thing it is called personification.

Example: *The sun smiled down on the trees as they stood to attention.*

Choose verbs and adverbs to make these nouns sound human.

windows		darkness	
the wind		leaves	
the machine		the television	
winter		sunlight	

Alliteration

Choose words for their sound as well as their meaning. Words with the same initial sound can create an interesting effect. This is called alliteration.

(1) Write an alliterative phrase you could use to make these descriptions effective.

- The sea

- A carriage

- The wind

(2) Write an alliterative phrase you could use to make these ideas memorable/effective.

- Save water

- Buy this pizza

Beware Do not overuse these techniques. One or two in each piece of writing is sufficient.

Spelling rules

The following sections cover words or rules where mistakes are commonly made. Make sure you know the rules and techniques to help you spell these words.

Plurals

You must be able to spell the plural form of words. Write the plural form of these words.

(1) family

(2) shelf

(3) disco

(4) journey

(5) attempt

(6) potato

(7) patch

(8) stripe

(9) tax

(10) nappy

Verb endings

You must be able to add *-ed*, *-ing* and *-s* endings to verbs like these.

Verb	Add *-ed*	Add *-ing*	Add *-s*
die			
tackle			
extend			
travel			
reply			
flutter			
survey			
realise			
gossip			
study			
control			
value			

Root words, prefixes and suffixes

You can use your knowledge of root words, prefixes and suffixes to help you spell lots of words. Make sure you know the spelling rules that help you to add prefixes and suffixes.

Write the correct spelling of these words.

nastyist		novelest	
cleverist		emptyer	
trickyer		speechles	
shamefull		pityful	
forgettful		actully	
stuby		murkey	
perfectley		scaley	
hungrly		unlikley	
originly		heavaly	
shakely		edable	
valuble		reverseable	
demonstrasion		attenshun	
extention		missplace	
ilegal		addmire	
immpolite		disatisfyed	
allready		Intanet	
micrascope		bycycle	
autamatick			

Reviewing your work

Checking – or reviewing – your work is an important part of being a writer. No writer finishes without rereading what has been written. There are always changes to be made – some are small and some are more significant. Without rereading your work, you could easily miss the opportunity to make some important alterations and improvements.

So, when you are reviewing your work, what should you be looking for?

- **Check that the main message of your writing has come through to the reader.** For example, if you are writing a suspense story, make sure that there is a feeling of anticipation and dread. If you are writing a persuasive piece, ask yourself, 'Would I be persuaded to change my mind, or at least reconsider my position, after reading this?' If not, perhaps you need to look again at the guidelines for persuasive writing.

- **Make sure you have followed the guidelines for the text type you have used.** It's very easy to slip into informal writing when you should be using something more formal. Reviewing helps you to pick up on those kinds of errors, which bring the standard of your writing down. If you are not sure if you have used the right language features or organisation, CHECK. Don't get worried about mistakes – just sort them out, and remember to correct that mistake in the future. REMEMBER, no one gets it right all the time, but you can choose to learn from your mistakes.

- **Check for basic spelling and grammar mistakes.** The easiest way to check for spelling is to reread your work, looking carefully as you read. If you come to a word that just doesn't look right, trust your instincts – it probably needs another attempt! Write out a few options on a piece of paper. Do any of them look right? Then, if you can, get a dictionary and check. Try to learn the correct spelling once you have looked it up. You won't always have the option of looking it up! As you check for basic grammar mistakes, the easiest way is to read your work out loud. If you listen carefully to what you are reading, you should be able to 'hear' sections or sentences that don't sound quite right. Try rewriting your sentence in several combinations, and read them out loud. Which one sounds right? Trust your instincts. Good writers are not scared of words!

- **Read as much as you can.** Read different types of books because it will help you to become accustomed to good writing. Then when you are checking your work, you will have a larger pool of ideas and phrases to draw on.

- **Always write down other writers' good ideas, sentences, phrases or words.** There's nothing wrong with using parts of someone else's ideas. Remember, there's nothing new under the sun. If you like the phrase or you think it might be useful, jot it down in your writer's notebook. You just never know when it could come in handy!

Writing and reading skills

Did you know that teachers are helping you develop your **writing** in at least eight ways? These are called 'assessment focuses' (AFs) and they are described here.

AF	Teacher language	This means...
1	Write imaginative, interesting and thoughtful texts	My writing is imaginative, interesting and thoughtful
2	Produce texts which are appropriate to the task, reader and purpose	I am able to write for different purposes and audiences according to the task set
3	Organise and present whole texts effectively, sequencing and structuring information, ideas and events	I can plan my writing and produce texts that sequence ideas, information and events within an appropriate structure
4	Construct paragraphs and use cohesion within and between paragraphs	I can use topic sentences and linking sentences to guide my reader through the text
5	Vary sentences for clarity, purpose and effect	I can use different types of sentences – simple, compound and complex – according to purpose and to create specific effects
6	Write with technical accuracy of syntax and punctuation in phrases, clauses and sentences	I am able to use different types of punctuation to make the meaning clear to my reader
7	Select appropriate and effective vocabulary	I can select and use a range of vocabulary, making choices according to purpose and audience
8	Use correct spelling	I can spell accurately

Reading is not just about being able to say and understand the words you see. Reading skills include the different ways you are expected to respond to a text. The seven assessment focuses for reading are:

AF	Teacher language	This means...
1	Use a range of strategies, including accurate decoding of text, to read for meaning	I can read for meaning
2	Understand, describe, select or retrieve information, events or ideas from texts and use quotations and references from texts	I can understand and pick out the appropriate quote, event or idea from a text and use PEE (Point, Evidence, Explain) to demonstrate my understanding
3	Deduce, infer or interpret information, events or ideas from texts	I can read and understand meaning that is only hinted at
4	Identify and comment on the structure and organisation of texts, including grammatical and presentational features at text level	I can identify the text type according to its presentational features and conventions. I can also comment on the writer's choice of text type to suit purpose
5	Explain and comment on the writer's use of language, including grammatical and literary features at word and sentence level	I can explain why the writer has made certain language choices (imperative verbs, emotive language, figurative language, formal/informal etc.)
6	Identify and comment on writers' purposes and viewpoints and the overall effect of a text on the reader	I can identify the writer's purpose and viewpoint and comment on how this affects the reader
7	Relate texts to their social, cultural and historical contexts and literary traditions	I can see how texts fit into their cultural and historical traditions

Reading comprehension

The Reading Test comes in the form of two booklets – one containing the texts you will read and another with the questions and space for your answers.

You have 1 hour for the test, including 15 minutes to read the booklets and 45 minutes to answer all the questions.

Reading the texts

Read the text in the booklet. DON'T RUSH. Make sure you read the contents page. It has key information which prepares you for the types of texts you will be reading, e.g.:

> A country of colour – a brief summary of how South Africa has changed in recent years.

If there are words you don't understand, read on and perhaps the paragraph will make sense anyway.

The reading test consists of different types of questions. Some of them are easy to answer (the information is right there) and some require you to apply some higher-level thinking skills. These are the Level 5 questions.

This table will help you to recognise the question types and identify how to answer them.

Type of question	How to recognise them	Skills needed
Literal	Who, what, when?	Answer is usually right there in text
Inference	Why, how?	'Read between the lines', what is hinted at
Deduction	Do you think?	Find evidence, clues to support you
Evaluation	Explain why…	Explain what makes something effective, successful, etc…
Authorial intent	The author uses… What is the effect of this?	Explain why the writer made these choices

Sometimes you may need to quote from the reading booklet to support your answer. For example:

I know that Miss Wileman is wealthy because it says in the text 'She had money coming out of her ears and for Miss Wileman, money really did grow on trees!'

Answering the questions

After you have read the question, look across in the margin and you will see how many marks the question is worth (these usually range from 1, 2 and 3 marks). This should help you to structure your answer. You must REFER TO THE TEXT in your answers. You can read the reading booklet as many times as you want! Although some of the questions require deep thinking, the answers will always relate to the reading booklet.

Pride and Prejudice

Jane Austen

This is the opening chapter from *Pride and Prejudice* by Jane Austen. The book is set in nineteenth-century England. Mrs Bennet is desperate for her five daughters to be married. However, her husband Mr Bennet does not share the same enthusiasm.

'My dear Mr Bennet,' said his lady to him one day, 'have you heard that Netherfield Park is let at last?'

Mr Bennet replied that he had not.

'But it is,' returned she; 'for Mrs. Long has just been here, and she told me all about it.'

Mr Bennet made no answer.

'Do not you want to know who has taken it?' cried his wife impatiently.

'*You* want to tell me, and I have no objection to hearing it.'

This was invitation enough.

'Why, my dear, you must know, Mrs Long says that Netherfield is taken by a young man of large fortune from the north of England; that he came down on Monday in a chaise and four to see the place, and was so much delighted with it that he agreed with Mr Morris immediately; that he is to take possession before Michaelmas, and some of his servants are to be in the house by the end of next week.'

'What is his name?'

'Bingley.'

'Is he married or single?'

'Oh! single, my dear, to be sure! A single man of large fortune; four or five thousand a year. What a fine thing for our girls!'

'How so? how can it affect them?'

'My dear Mr Bennet,' replied his wife, 'how can you be so tiresome! You must know that I am thinking of his marrying one of them.'

'Is that his design in settling here?'

'Design! nonsense, how can you talk so! But it is very likely that he *may* fall in love with one of them, and therefore you must visit him as soon as he comes.'

'I see no occasion for that. You and the girls may go, or you may send them by themselves, which perhaps will be still better; for, as you are as handsome as any of them, Mr Bingley might like you the best of the party.'

Glossary

chaise and four – a carriage with horses

Michaelmas – the feast of St Michael celebrated in September

large fortune – lots of money

design – plan

If you need more space for your answers use extra paper.

1 Why does Darren need 19–20 books for the Darren Shan saga?

AF3 ☐ 1

1 mark

2 Find and copy a phrase which shows Darren had mixed feelings about his previous job in Limerick.

AF3 ☐ 2

1 mark

3 Give **two** ways in which the character of Darren Shan is different from the real Darren Shan, the author.

AF2 ☐ 3

2 marks

4 This interview is clear to read because it is divided into questions and answers. How does this layout help the reader?

AF4 ☐ 4

2 marks

5 Why do you think Darren Shan's publisher wanted to publish this interview on its website?

AF6 ☐ 5

2 marks

6 Give **three** of the things a writer should do to be sure of success, according to Darren Shan.

AF2 ☐ 6

3 marks

Total marks ☐

Interview with Darren Shan

Darren Shan is an Irish author who is most famous for having written *The Saga of Darren Shan*. His books have won many awards including the WHSmith children's book of the year and the Irish children's book of the year award. This interview is taken from his publisher's website.

How many books will there be in the Darren Shan saga?

It's a big long series. It covers a lot of time, there are lots of other characters, more are introduced in later books and some are killed off. I don't know the exact number, but there will be somewhere in the region of 19 or 20 books. It's a crazy undertaking, but that's how long it's going to take to tell the story.

Did you know that there would be several books in the series?

Cirque Du Freak was going to be a single book. I also write adult books and this was the first time I had written a children's book so I had no idea whether it was going to work or not. I did know it was going to have an open-ended finish, so that there might be room for one or two sequels, but I had no idea it was going to be such a big long series. It was really when I was writing book two and planning book three that I thought a series was coming in to place.

How do you think up the names for the characters in your books?

They come from different places. Mr Crepsley came from taking the word Mr Creepy. When I first had the idea for *Cirque Du Freak* he was going to be called Mr Creepy and his performing tarantula Madame Octa, but I thought Mr Creepy was far too childish for so serious a character, but I liked the sound of it so I started playing around with it and put a few extra letters in. That happens with loads of names; some will be ordinary names which I'll take and juggle around with, some will be words that I've played around with. They come from different places. Some of the characters will have ordinary names. I enjoy playing around with vampire names and making them sound mysterious.

Is the character of Darren Shan in the book similar to you?

He is similar in many ways; obviously I use the same name that I write under. I've got to admit that he is a much more noble character than I am. He's much braver than me, much tougher than me, especially the decision he makes in book one to sacrifice his own life for his friend's life. At that age I think very few kids would choose.

What other jobs have you had?

The only other long-term job I've had was working for a cable company back in Limerick installing things like Sky Sports (working on a computer turning on people's Sky Sports and movies and disconnecting them if they hadn't paid). That was quite fun as well, but it was also quite horrific.

What are your best tips for budding writers?

The best tip I have is to keep writing. The more you write the better you get. There is no magic involved, there is no secret formula. It's simply a case of the more you write, the more you learn, the better you get. If you're determined to be an author and stick with it the chances are excellent that you will succeed. Very few people actually fail if they set out to be an author, most who do give up if they're not making it. Take rejection on the chin, but keep writing and you will succeed.

If you need more space for your answers use extra paper.

1 What **two** gifts are promised to help make children really want to go on the Fun Day?

_____

AF2 [ ] 1
1 mark

2 If you do not want to use the online booking form, how else can you book a place for a child to go on the Falcon Fun Day?

_____

AF2 [ ] 2
1 mark

3 Look at the paragraph beginning with '_The Falcon Fun Day begins at 10 a.m..._'. Find and copy a short phrase which means the experience is genuine and authentic.

_____

AF2 [ ] 3
1 mark

4 What is the purpose of the photographs on this website?

_____

_____

AF4 [ ] 4
1 mark

5 Can these children take part in the Children's Falcon Fun Days at Leeds Castle? Write _Yes_ or _No_ by their names:

John, aged 11 _____

Fatima, aged 7 _____

Max, aged 9 _____

Daisy, aged 8 _____

AF3 [ ] 5
2 marks

6 Imagine you have been to visit Leeds Castle. Write what you would say about your experience.

_____

_____

_____

_____

AF7 [ ] 6
2 marks

7 Why has the author of this web page included quotations in this text?

_____

_____

_____

_____

AF6 [ ] 7
3 marks

Total marks [ ]

Falcon Fun Days

The Hawking Centre at Leeds Castle in Kent has a collection of birds of prey for visitors to see. This page is adapted from their website.

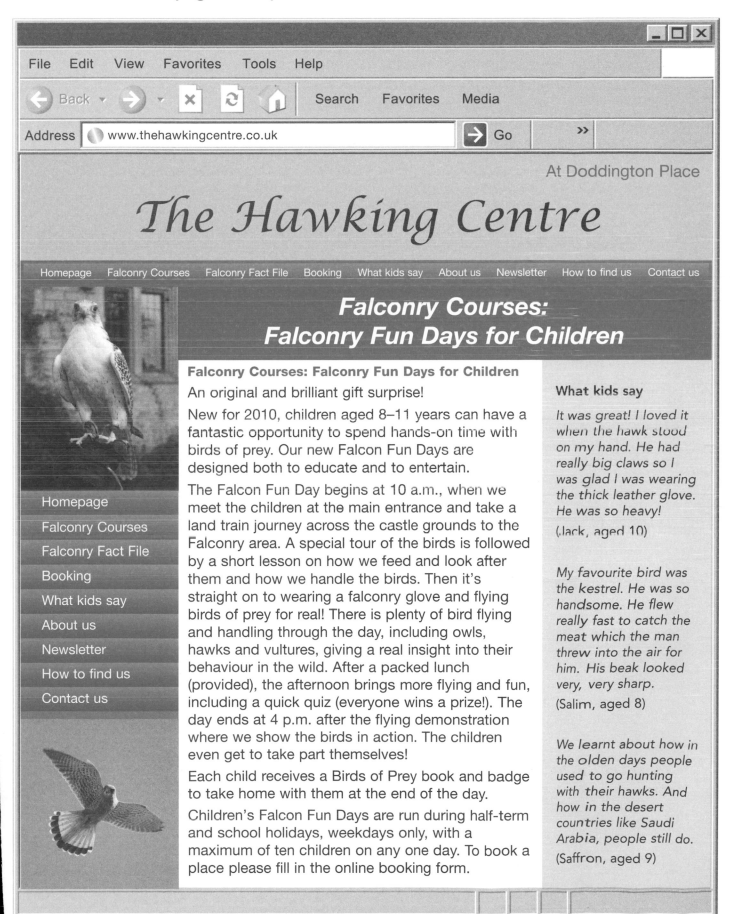

File   Edit   View   Favorites   Tools   Help

Back   ×   Search   Favorites   Media

Address www.thehawkingcentre.co.uk   Go   »

At Doddington Place

The Hawking Centre

Homepage   Falconry Courses   Falconry Fact File   Booking   What kids say   About us   Newsletter   How to find us   Contact us

Falconry Courses: Falconry Fun Days for Children

- Homepage
- Falconry Courses
- Falconry Fact File
- Booking
- What kids say
- About us
- Newsletter
- How to find us
- Contact us

Falconry Courses: Falconry Fun Days for Children

An original and brilliant gift surprise!

New for 2010, children aged 8–11 years can have a fantastic opportunity to spend hands-on time with birds of prey. Our new Falcon Fun Days are designed both to educate and to entertain.

The Falcon Fun Day begins at 10 a.m., when we meet the children at the main entrance and take a land train journey across the castle grounds to the Falconry area. A special tour of the birds is followed by a short lesson on how we feed and look after them and how we handle the birds. Then it's straight on to wearing a falconry glove and flying birds of prey for real! There is plenty of bird flying and handling through the day, including owls, hawks and vultures, giving a real insight into their behaviour in the wild. After a packed lunch (provided), the afternoon brings more flying and fun, including a quick quiz (everyone wins a prize!). The day ends at 4 p.m. after the flying demonstration where we show the birds in action. The children even get to take part themselves!

Each child receives a Birds of Prey book and badge to take home with them at the end of the day.

Children's Falcon Fun Days are run during half-term and school holidays, weekdays only, with a maximum of ten children on any one day. To book a place please fill in the online booking form.

What kids say

It was great! I loved it when the hawk stood on my hand. He had really big claws so I was glad I was wearing the thick leather glove. He was so heavy!

(Jack, aged 10)

My favourite bird was the kestrel. He was so handsome. He flew really fast to catch the meat which the man threw into the air for him. His beak looked very, very sharp.

(Salim, aged 8)

We learnt about how in the olden days people used to go hunting with their hawks. And how in the desert countries like Saudi Arabia, people still do.

(Saffron, aged 9)

ABOUT THE READING TEST

In the Reading Test you will find questions that ask you to:

- **select relevant information and quotations from the text** (e.g. *Write down two ways … Fill in the facts about … Find and copy two words that …*)

Tip	★ Sometimes the information is from different places in the text.

- **deduce and infer information or ideas from texts** (e.g. *Why do you think …? How do you know …? Why is …?*)

Tip	★ Words like *suggest, imply, what do you think* are often clues that the question will need you to infer. But other questions may also need inference and deduction. Explain the thinking behind your answer.

- **comment on how the text is structured, organised and presented** (e.g. *Why has the author used …? What is the purpose of …?*)

Tip	★ Explain precisely why a feature is used in the text you have read (not just in texts generally).

- **analyse the writer's use of language** (e.g. *What does this tell us …? How was the effect created?*)

Tip	★ Explain exactly why particular words were chosen and describe their effects fully. Sometimes words, similes and metaphors have different levels of meaning that you need to explain.

- **identify the writer's purpose or viewpoint** (e.g. *What is the purpose of …? What does the writer think about …?*)

Tip	★ You need to take a general overview of the text to identify the author's main purpose.

- **comment on the effect of the text on you, or on readers in general** (e.g. *Did you find the text effective? Would adults find the information helpful?*)

Tip	★ These questions sound simple, but to answer them fully you need to comment on several key aspects of the text to support your response, e.g. content, style, writer's purpose.

- **relate/compare the text to other texts** (e.g. *In what way is this like …? Could this be described as …?*)

Tip	★ Look for similarities and differences and then explain your ideas. A good answer will need more than one point, so make each point, give an example and explain it. If you are comparing two texts, make sure you refer to both.

If you need more space for your answers use extra paper.

1 Who told Mrs Bennet that a gentleman was renting Netherfield Park?

_____

AF2

1

1 mark

2 What is the name of the man moving to Netherfield Park?

_____

AF2

2

1 mark

3 Find the sentence which suggests that Mrs Bennet needs little encouragement to continue talking?

_____

AF6

3

1 mark

4 Jane Austen writes that 'Mr Bennet made no answer'. What does this tell us about Mr Bennet?

_____

_____

AF5

4

2 marks

5 When Mrs Bennet says 'Why, my dear ... by the end of next week.', there is no full stop in this paragraph. What does Jane Austen want us to think about Mrs Bennet?

_____

_____

AF6

5

2 marks

6 Give an example from the text explaining how it shows that Mr Bennet enjoys teasing Mrs Bennet.

_____

_____

AF5

6

2 marks

7 Tick **three** examples which demonstrate that this novel is set over 200 years ago.

Mrs Bennet calls her husband Mr Bennet. ☐

Mr Bennet teases his wife. ☐

Bingley earns between four and five thousand a year. ☐

Bingley arrives in a chaise and four. ☐

Mrs Bennet is a chatterbox. ☐

AF7

7

3 marks

Total marks

51

First day at school

Roger McGough

In this poem Roger McGough imagines what it would be like for a small child to go to school for the first time. He writes from the child's point of view.

A millionbillionwillion miles from home
Waiting for the bell to go. (To go where?)
Why are they all so big, other children?
So noisy? So much at home they
Must have been born in uniform
Lived all their lives in playgrounds
Spent the years inventing games
That don't let me in. Games
That are rough, that swallow you up.

And the railings.
All around, the railings.
Are they to keep out wolves and monsters?
Things that carry off and eat children?
Things you don't take sweets from?
Perhaps they're to stop us getting out
Running away from the lessins. Lessin.
What does a lessin look like?
Sounds small and slimy.
They keep them in the glassrooms.
Whole rooms made out of glass. Imagine.

I wish I could remember my name
Mummy said it would come in useful.
Like wellies. When there's puddles.
Yellowwellies. I wish she was here.
I think my name is sewn on somewhere
Perhaps the teacher will read it for me.
Tea-cher. The one who makes the tea.

If you need more space for your answers use extra paper.

1 What does the writer of the poem think children are born wearing?

_____

AF2
1
1 mark

2 'A millionbillionwillion miles from home'. What is the effect of this description?

_____

AF5
2
1 mark

3 In the second verse the child looks at the railings and wonders what they are for. Tick **two** answers which summarise their thoughts.

The railings are there to make the school look friendly. ☐

The railings protect the school. ☐

The railings stop children from escaping. ☐

The railings are cages for the wolves. ☐

AF3
3
2 marks

4 This poem portrays the thoughts of a young child. Why do you think Roger McGough chose to use short and incomplete sentences throughout the poem?

_____

_____

AF4
4
2 marks

5 Many reception teachers read this poem to their classes. Explain why you think they choose this poem.

_____

_____

AF6
5
2 marks

6 Roger McGough uses humour and language for different functions in this poem. Match the quotation to its function.

Quotation	Function
Tea-cher. The one who makes the tea.	To describe how alone the child feels.
I wish she was here.	To show the child's misunderstanding of some words.
And the railings. All around, the railings.	To emphasise how trapped and frightened the child is.

AF6
6
3 marks

Total marks

53

Seasick

Nick Toczek

This poem plays with the sounds and meanings of words. It is set under water where a squid doesn't feel 'whelk' and the 'doctopus' is trying to help.

'I don't feel whelk,' whaled the squid, sole-fully.
'What's up?' asked the doctopus.
'I've got sore mussels and a tummy-hake,' she told him.

'Lie down and I'll egg salmon you.' mermaid the doctopus.
'Rays your voice,' said the squid. 'I'm a bit hard of herring.'
'Sorry! I didn't do it on porpoise.' replied the doctopus orcwardly.

He helped her to oyster self on to his couch
And asked her to look up so he could sea urchin.
He soon flounder plaice that hurt.

'This'll make it eel,' he said, whiting a prescription.
'So I won't need to see the sturgeon?' she asked.
'Oh no,' he told her. 'Ina couple of dace you'll feel brill.'

'Cod bless you,' she said.
'That'll be sick squid,' replied the doctopus.

If you need more space for your answers use extra paper.

1 In the poem, who doesn't feel well and has gone to see the doctor?

_____

2 List **four** examples of different sea creatures in this poem.

_____

_____

_____

3 This poem was written to be performed. Explain what the difference is between performing this and reading it silently to yourself.

_____

_____

4 In a review Nick Toczek was described as: 'The greatest success was without doubt "Mr Dynamite", the Englishman Nick Toczek whose performance of all-round writings exploded like a firework.' How do you think the poet would perform this poem? (Think about his voice, body language, moving round the stage, props.)

_____

_____

_____

5 'Lie down and I'll egg salmon you,' mermaid the doctopus. The poet uses a mixture of land-words and sea-words. Complete the table below.

Sea-word	Land-word
egg salmon you	examine you
doctopus	
orcwardly	
sick squid	

AF2

1

1 mark

AF5

2

2 marks

AF7

3

2 marks

AF7

4

3 marks

AF5

5

3 marks

Total marks

55